# COLDPLAY LIVE 2

Presented to Kaz
on his 21st Birthday
by Steve O'Rourke
and Sam Shortis
May your bathdays be very happy
forevermore.

Dude! you ROCK!!
Thanks for the Cherries and your
mind bending company.
Massive Love to ya.
                    x x

**Wise Publications**
part of The Music Sales Group

London / New York / Paris / Sydney / Copenhagen / Berlin / Madrid / Tokyo

Published by:
Wise Publications,
8/9 Frith Street, London W1D 3JB, England.

Exclusive distributors:
Music Sales Limited,
Distribution Centre, Newmarket Road, Bury St. Edmunds,
Suffolk IP33 3YB, England.

Music Sales Pty Limited,
120 Rothschild Avenue, Rosebery,
NSW 2018, Australia.

Order No. AM979770
ISBN 1-84449-420-9
This book © Copyright 2004 by Wise Publications.

Music arrangements by Derek Jones.
Music processed by Paul Ewers Music Design.

Printed in the United Kingdom by Caligraving Limited, Thetford, Norfolk.

www.musicsales.com

Your Guarantee of Quality:
As publishers, we strive to produce every book
to the highest commercial standards.

Whilst endeavouring to retain the original running order of
the recorded album, the book has been carefully designed to minimise
awkward page turns and to make playing from it a real pleasure.

Particular care has been given to specifying acid-free, neutral-sized paper
made from pulps which have not been elemental chlorine bleached.

This pulp is from farmed sustainable forests
and was produced with special regard for the environment.

Throughout, the printing and binding have been planned to ensure a sturdy,
attractive publication which should give years of enjoyment.

If your copy fails to meet our high standards, please inform us
and we will gladly replace it.

# Politik

*Words & Music by Guy Berryman, Jon Buckland, Will Champion & Chris Martin*

9

Verse 2:
Give me one, 'cause one is best
In confusion confidence
Give me peace of mind and trust
Don't forget the rest of us.
Give me strength, reserve, control
Give me heart and give me soul
Wounds that heal, and cracks that fix
Tell me your own politik.

And open up your eyes *etc.*

# God Put A Smile Upon Your Face

*Words & Music by Guy Berryman, Jon Buckland, Will Champion & Chris Martin*

13

I've got to say I'm on my way_____ down.

God give me style and give me grace._____

God put a

smile up-on my face._____

your guess_____ is as good____ as_____

mine._____

*Guitar*

*Verse 2:*
Where do we go to draw the line?
I've got to say I wasted all your time honey, honey
Where do I go to fall from grace?
God put a smile upon your face, yeah.

*Verse 3:*
Where do we go, nobody knows
Don't ever say you're on your way down, when
God gave you style and gave you grace
And put a smile upon your face.

Now when you work it out *etc.*

# A Rush Of Blood To The Head

Words & Music by Guy Berryman, Jon Buckland, Will Champion & Chris Martin

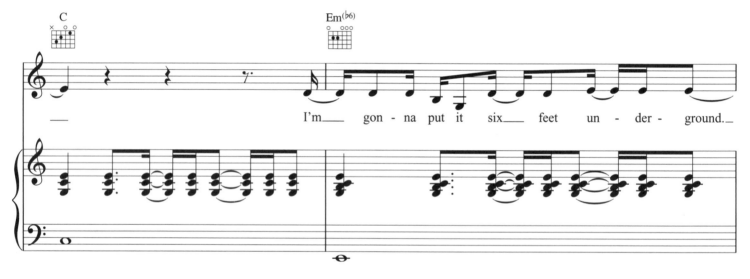

if____ you can tell me some - thing worth____ fight - ing for.

Oh, and I'm____ gon - na buy this place,____ is what I____ say,____

blame it up - on a rush____ of blood to the head.____ Hon -

-ey, all the move - ments you're start - ing to make,____ see me crum -

23

Start as you___ mean to go on.___

To Coda

4.He said I'm___

___ gon - na buy this place___ and see it go.___

Stand___

___ here be - side my ba - by, watch the___ or - ange glow.

Oh, meet me on___ the road, oh, meet me where___ I___ ___ said. Blame it all___ up-on___ a rush of blood___ to the head.

# Daylight

Words & Music by Guy Berryman, Jon Buckland, Will Champion & Chris Martin

*Verse 2:*
On a hilltop
On a sky-rise
Like a first-born child
On the full tilt
And in full flight
Defeat darkness
Breaking daylight.

Ooh and the sun will shine *etc.*

# Trouble

Words & Music by Guy Berryman, Jon Buckland, Will Champion & Chris Martin

35

and thought of all the stu-pid things I'd said.

2. Oh no, what's this? A spi-der web and I'm caught in the mid - dle.
3. Oh no, I see, a spi-der web and it's me in the mid - dle.

So I turned to run, and thought of all the stu-pid things I'd
So I twist, and turn, but here am I in my lit-tle bub-

They spun a web___

# One I Love

Words & Music by Guy Berryman, Jon Buckland, Will Champion & Chris Martin

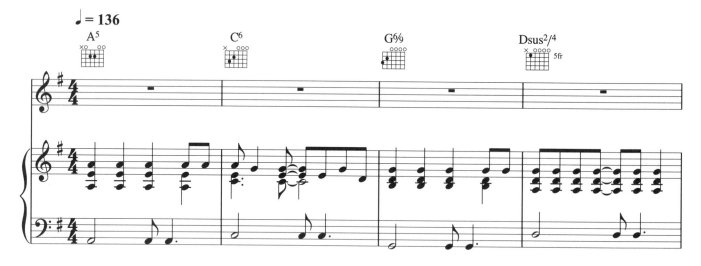

43

44

# Don't Panic

Words & Music by Guy Berryman, Jon Buckland, Will Champion & Chris Martin

1, 2. Bones, sink-ing like stones, all __ that we've fought __ for. __
*(Verse 3 Instrumental)*

Homes, pla - ces we've grown, all __ of us are

Oh, all— that I know, there's no-thing here to run from,— cos

yeah, ev-'ry-bo-dy here's got some-bo-dy to lean on.—

# Shiver

Words & Music by Guy Berryman, Jon Buckland, Will Champion & Chris Martin

Guitar tuned:

① = D♯  ④ = B

② = B  ⑤ = A

③ = G  ⑥ = E

look in your di - rec - tion but you pay me no at - ten - tion___ do you?___

*(Verse 2 see block lyric)*

And I

know you don't lis - ten to me cos you say you see straight through me___ don't

you?

But on and on___

Verse 2:
So you know how much I need you
But you never even see me do you?
And is this my final chance of getting you?

But on and on, from the moment I wake *etc.*

# See You Soon

Words & Music by Guy Berryman, Jon Buckland, Will Champion & Chris Martin

# Moses

Words & Music by Guy Berryman, Jon Buckland, Will Champion & Chris Martin

65

# Yellow

Words & Music by Guy Berryman, Jon Buckland, Will Champion & Chris Martin

*Verse 2:*
I swam across, I jumped across for you
Oh, what a thing to do
Cos you were all yellow
I drew a line, I drew a line for you
Oh, what a thing to do
And it was all yellow.

Your skin, oh yeah, your skin and bones
Turn into something beautiful
And you know, for you I'd bleed myself dry
For you I'd bleed myself dry.

# Everything's Not Lost

Words & Music by Guy Berryman, Jon Buckland, Will Champion & Chris Martin

hop - ing ev - 'ry -thing's not lost._____

well, I'll be coun - ting up my___ de - mons yeah,___

___ hop - ing ev - 'ry - thing's___ not lost.___

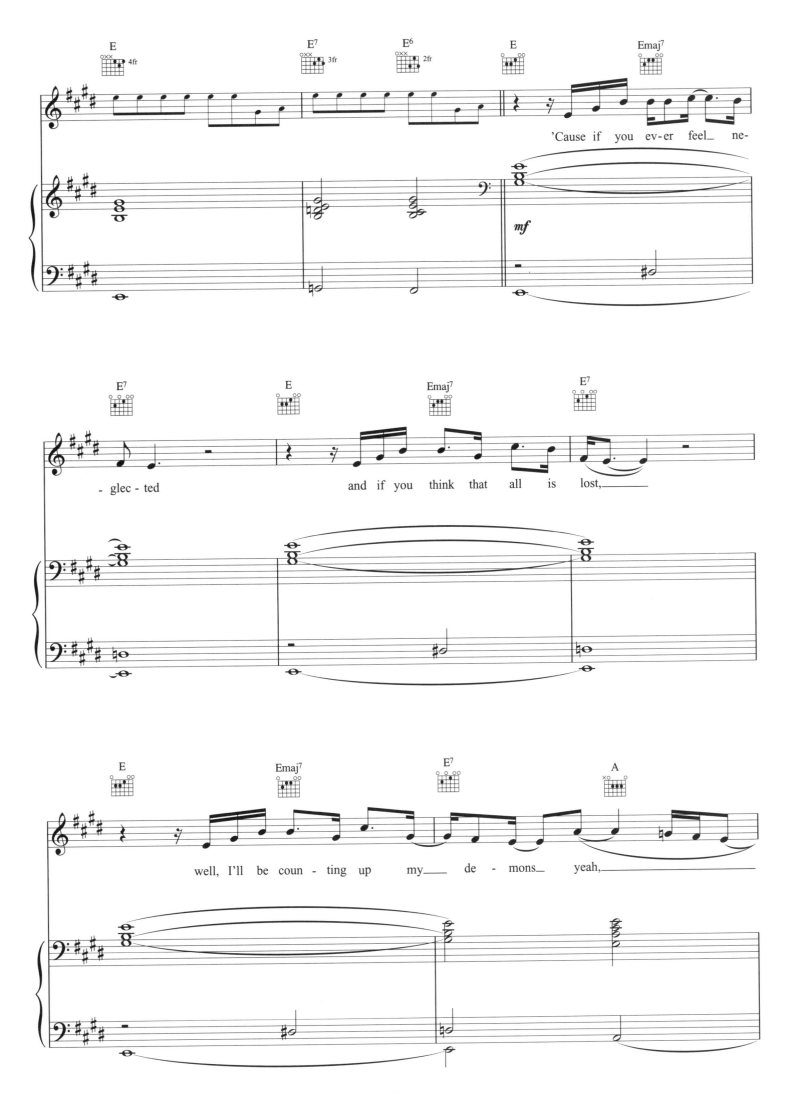

# The Scientist

Words & Music by Guy Berryman, Jon Buckland, Will Champion & Chris Martin

1. Come up to meet___ you, tell you I'm sor - ry, you don't know how love-
*(Verse 2 see block lyric)*

*Verse 2:*
I was just guessing at numbers and figures
Pulling your puzzles apart.
Questions of science, science and progress
That must speak as loud as my heart.
Tell me you love me, come back and haunt me
Oh, and I rush to the start
Running in circles, chasing our tails
Coming back as we are.

Nobody said it was easy *etc.*

# Clocks

Words & Music by Guy Berryman, Jon Buckland, Will Champion & Chris Martin

1. The lights go out and I can't be saved, tides that I tried to

*(Verse 2 see block lyric)*

And no - thing else com - pares.

And no - thing else com - pares.

Verse 2:
Confusion that never stops
The closing walls and the ticking clocks
Gonna come back and take you home
I could not stop that you now know, singing...
Come out upon my seas
Cursed missed opportunities
Am I a part of the cure?
Or I am a part of the disease, singing...

You are *etc.*

# In My Place

Words & Music by Guy Berryman, Jon Buckland, Will Champion & Chris Martin

1. In my place, in my____ place were lines that I____ could-n't
(Verse 2 see block lyric)

*Verse 2:*
I was scared, I was scared
Tired and under-prepared
But I'll wait for it.
And if you go, if you go
And leave me down here on my own
Then I'll wait for you, yeah.

Yeah, how long must you wait *etc.*

# Amsterdam

Words & Music by Guy Berryman, Jon Buckland, Will Champion & Chris Martin

my star is fad - ing and I_____ swerve out of con - trol._____

If_____ I'd_____ if I'd on - ly wait - ed I'd not be stuck here in this_____ hole._____

2. Come here, oh,
*(Verse 3 see block lyric)*

*Verse 3:*
Come on, oh, my star is fading
And I see no chance of release
And I know I'm dead on the surface
But I am screaming underneath.

And time is on your side *etc.*

# Life Is For Living

Words & Music by Guy Berryman, Jon Buckland, Will Champion & Chris Martin

'Cause in the end there's on - ly us.